IMBAL

AN EXPERIMENTAL
COLLECTION
OF
MICRO STORIES & POETRY

II

IMBALANCE

AN EXPERIMENTAL COLLECTION
OF
MICRO STORIES & POETRY

By

Christine McGuigan

EASY BREAK, FIRST TIME PUBLISHING • DEDICATED TO ACCEPTANCE AND RECOGNITION •

TM

Easy Break, First Time Publishing
Cupertino

ISBN: 1-891571-00-1

Printed in the United States of America

DEDICATIONS

To Richard for his friendship, loyalty, and love

To my parents, Jack & Rosemary for giving me life

To Angie for her courage

ACKNOWLEDGMENTS

Special thanks to the earth—my mother, to Paul Leckner for always believing in me, and to Vin Cook at The Bayonne Writers' Group for his dedication to the craft of writing. I give thanks also to those who have inspired me, especially the Plains Native Americans, Raymond Carver, Hubert Selby Jr., Sylvia Plath, Edgar Allan Poe, Black Elk, John (Fire) Lame Deer, Rod Serling, Charles Beaumont, George Orwell, my family, and The Doors—Jim, Ray, Robby, and John.

Author photo by Richard Bruness. Cover art concept by Christine McGuigan.

PROLOGUE

All I ever wanted to be was a writer. The problem was I didn't want to write romance novels or trendy articles on the latest breakthroughs on lipo-suction and breast-jobs or cute tidbits on the "hottest" looks for fashion. No, I wanted to write about all these things people were doing to the earth and themselves. I found out later on that I was and am more of a poet at heart than a writer and have been both blessed and cursed with this (I have a martyr mind-set that I'll never break!).

Another problem was the lack of opportunity available for people like me to share our work with the public. The big conglomerates are wiping the small presses out into oblivion and it's censorship and mind control corporate style. Look, there's room for all of us here and while the Kathy Lee Giffords of the world have their place, so do the people like me—the antithesis of her kind.

My goal is to expose you to a writing style that differs from the norm. The micro story is a literary form I created. It differs from the short-short because the micro story, like the great circle the Native Americans taught me about, has no beginning, middle, or end. The haiku and senryu poems in this collection were written without rhyme in the 3 line 5/7/5 style, typical of the traditional haiku and senryu. My choice of words and the images the words create are in contrast to the austerity found in the traditional haiku and senryu. Out of respect for the traditionalists, I have branded my poems as experimental.

Some of the poems came to me in dreams. For example, I was haunted by images of bombs exploding in a desert and by a woman with "bruised, lined eyes." Others were written from observations and experiences. These images dominated my thoughts to the point where I had to exorcise them from mind to paper. Welcome to the pages of my soul.

Christine McGuigan
Lyndhurst, New Jersey
March 19, 1997

Imbalance *(noun)* *lack of balance: the state of being out of equilibrium or out of proportion*

The Merriam-Webster Dictionary

IMBALANCE

It happened at my cousin's baby shower. I'd been home only three months since my two years of relief work in Somalia, and I wasn't ready to see my relatives and friends after what I had been through. But, my mother insisted that I be social and attend Francine's shower and I was just too weak to argue.

I was greeted at the restaurant by my Aunt Anna who said, "Welcome back to the *real* world." I tried to bite my tongue but blurted, "Yea, you're right, Aunt Anna. This is the real world. The world where innocent children die of starvation because their government fucks them over, doesn't exist, right?"

My mother put her hands on my shoulder and said, "Aunt Anna, you'll have to excuse Sara, she's still re-adjusting." She pulled me away from Aunt Anna and told me to sit at the table with my other cousins.

Everyone kept commenting on how thin and drawn I looked and each of them made it a point to inquire about the acne I developed in Somalia. I forgot how rude our culture is. People somehow think it's fitting conversation to give you a detailed critique of your physical appearance.

I sat through all the meaningless chit-chat and I felt like I had nothing in common with these people who I had known and loved for years. I couldn't relate to their conversations about car phone bills and French manicures. My perception of everything changed in Somalia. I had children die in my arms! My nightmares are still filled with their bony faces and swollen stomachs. One child vomited on me right before he died and for a moment, I thought I saw his soul leave his tiny body. It was a horrifying, enlightening experience that left me with no tolerance for pretense.

My hands started to shake when my cousin Francine walked into our section of the restaurant.

"Surprise!" The crowd yelled and she seemed surprised or at least pretended to be. But, her appearance made me think of a pregnant woman I found dead outside of a homemade tent. Her face was shriveled from the sun and her plump belly looked as though it would've exploded if she had lived. It contained a dead child who was spared the pain of living in poverty.

After endless greetings, we sat down to eat, and after more conversation that I couldn't relate to, our dinner ended. Yet, heaps and globs of food remained on their plates. This food could have saved that pregnant woman!

Aren't you going to finish that?" I asked my cousin Gina.

"No, I'm full."

"You should take it home. They'll wrap it for you."

"Why don't you mind your own business? You can't change the world, so why bother?" Gina glared at me. The sight of the three gold chains around her neck made me sick. I thought about how the gold miners in South Africa destroy precious land and exploit their workers because of pure greed.

"What gives you the right to waste that food?!" I yelled. Our side of the room in the restaurant we had rented for the shower grew quiet.

"Grow up, Sara. You want to help someone? Help yourself. Get a real job and leave me alone."

"Answer my question. What gives you the right to waste that food?"

My mother came running over to our table and again, made excuses for me. I'm twenty seven years old, yet ever since I returned from Somalia, she's been treating me like a fragile child.

"Gina, Sara's not picking a fight with you. She's seen a lot. It's hard for her to see food wasted. Please girls, don't ruin Francine's special day!"

"I'm getting the hell away from you. You've lost your mind and manners out in that desert!" Gina threw her dinner napkin on the table, grabbed her Gucci bag, and left to change tables.

Present opening time. Francine received a bundle of clothing, baby blankets, an air purifier, a basin, two intercom sets, and plenty of other things that I lost track of. She also received this contraption that actually heats the baby wipes so they're not cold when they rub against the baby's skin. For some reason, this gift really pushed me over the edge. I thought about the young children who died in my arms. No one cared about their deaths, let alone if they ever had a warm fucking baby wipe. These children rarely even had clothing! This imbalance consumed me.

I felt the tears trickle down my cheeks and that's all I can remember. Next thing I know, I'm in here—trying to come to terms with what I've experienced and clinging to what little sanity I have left.

In the fire's wake, I
saw your ghost...you blew a kiss
to me and vanished.

Beside your coffin
I kneel and kiss your cheek...still
praying for your soul

Wolves howl in darkness
Hunters with assault rifles
Gunshots fill the air

WOLF

Majestic creature, you have been wronged!
Those howls were a soulful, poetic song
But, they ignored your primal, weeping cries
The sadness, forever frozen in your eyes

You gave them their most loyal friend
And still, they betrayed you in the end
Swift like the wind, pure like the sun
I wish I could change what they have done

You cared for your young and protected the pack
Oh, I would give my soul to bring you back!
The symbol of freedom is now a victim of greed
How could anyone commit such a horrible deed?

WHORE

"Have you sold any paintings lately?" Paul asked. He had his arm around me and I almost started to cry. I couldn't let myself do that so I pushed his arm off of me.

"If I did then I wouldn't be doing this." I sat up in the bed and finished the rest of my scotch.

"They'll sell, you'll see." He rose from the bed and started to put on his clothes.

"I'm not in it for the money, you know. I need it to live but painting is my life."

"I know, I understand. You need to think about your future though. Are you saving money?"

"No." I poured myself another drink.

"Why not, Jessie? Is this what you want to be doing for the rest of your life?" I watched him button his shirt. He was a tall, slender man in his early forties with a full head of dark, graying hair.

"What do you care? You got what you wanted so why don't you leave me alone? Your phony concern really confuses me. Nobody else does this caring number except you."

"It's not a routine, I care about you. You're a talented young girl. I don't want to see you broken and tortured like so many other artists in this town."

"I'm already broken and tortured."

"And we both know what comes next. I don't want to see that happen."

"Thank you for your concern but I can't open my heart to you. Don't do this to me. Just meet me here, pay me, fuck me, and leave!"

"Why are you mad at me for caring about you?" He fixed his tie and sat next to me on the bed.

"Because I find myself thinking about you during the day. I look forward to seeing you. You're the only one who's nice to me and you're screwing my mind up. I'm just your whore, not your lover and I won't let you break my heart."

"I have a thing for you, Jessie. You're much more to me than a whore. I'm starting to resent your other customers; I want you all to myself."

"Go home to your wife, Paul!" I stood up and unlocked the hotel room door.

"I hate leaving you. I do care about you but I love my wife. You're more to me than a whore, Jessie."

"Please go now. It would be best for me if you did."

"I'll meet you again here next week." He went to kiss me but I pulled away.

"See you Tuesday," he added. He grabbed his suit jacket and blew a kiss to me.

"Good-bye," I said. He left and I locked the hotel room door. I almost cried but I fought it. My stomach ached from the scotch but I poured myself another drink. I deserved the pain.

Daisies in her hair
drinking tequila, tears bleed
from her bruised, lined eyes

Woman on the pier,
throws her ring into the sea.
Smiles as the tears flow.

Punk-Rock vampire girl
Waits for a john on the strip
Chain-smokes between tricks

The boardwalk at night—
mist rising from the sea...he
devours her neck.

POWER
The battle for your brain

LEARNING
A teacher's failed lesson

VIOLENCE
Viruses a web of celluloid
breakdown
on the road to freedom

OPEN THE DOOR
to your mind

and
LEARN
learn how to overcome

The storm brought to shore
the tampons and needles dumped
by the hospital

By the casino,
old, intoxicated man
begs me for money.

ATLANTIC CITY

"Hi, honey, I'm back," a heavy-set elderly woman said to the dollar slot machine. She opened her faded, white, canvas tote bag and took out two rolls of coins.

"You're going to help me again this year, isn't that right?" She spoke loudly and the young man sitting next to her listened to her talking to the machine.

"Here goes nothin'!" She put three dollar coins in the machine and pulled the lever. Two bars and one diamond. No coins came out.

"That's all right. We're just warming up." She pulled the lever again and again. Ten coins came out of the machine.

"I knew I could count on you!" She continued to feed the machine three coins at a time. Twenty coins came out this time.

"Yes! I have a feeling about you tonight!" The woman wiped her forehead with a tissue and took out another roll of coins.

"Help me my friend. No one will help me...not my children, not the government. You're the only one I can count on." She fed the machine coin after coin.

The young man sitting next to her looked as though he was agitated. He collected the few coins that remained in the tray and left. The moment he left the chair, a middle aged woman with bleached hair and blue eye shadow took his place.

"I feel lucky tonight!" The middle aged woman yelled. She took out six rolls of dollar coins from her over-sized purse and placed them in the tray under the slot machine.

"You're only testing me, I know that," the elderly woman said to the machine, "I'll keep at it, I won't leave you. You're the *only* machine I play." Again, she fed the machine.

After an hour, the elderly woman was out of change. She pressed the change button and an attendant cashed her fifty dollar bill for coins. She fed the machine again and again.

The elderly woman had ten coins left so she played only one coin at a time. She shook her head at the results.

"What's going on? I need you to help me! Please!" She yelled. Two people behind her turned to see what she was yelling about.

The middle aged woman pressed the change button and took out a one hundred dollar bill. She lit a cigarette and waited for the change attendant. She wore a gold studded sweater with black and gold studded pants to match.

"I'm gonna' win, I can *feel* it," the middle aged woman said.

The elderly woman sat in the chair by her favorite machine even though she had no coins left.

"Hey lady, are you playing this machine?" An unkempt, middle aged man with a blemished complexion asked.

She said nothing.

"Hey, this is my lucky machine. If you're not playing then you have to get up!" He commanded.

The elderly woman remained silent.

The unkempt man waved to a security guard and asked him to tell the elderly woman to leave.

"Ma'am, are you playing this machine?" The security guard asked.

She gave no response.

"Ma'am, if you're not playing the machine then you have to leave the seat and give someone else a chance to play."

She remained silent.

"Ma'am, if you will not leave politely, then I will have you removed from the seat."

The security guard spoke into his two way radio .... Three minutes later two muscular, tall men picked the elderly woman off of the seat. They carried her out the exit and put her and the canvas tote bag on the curb of the street.

She sat there for a while, not making a sound. She bit her bottom lip and a tear streamed down her weathered face.

A pass for big druggies
CLERIC'S LONG ORDEAL ENDS

Shrink turns losers
into real winners

JUDGE GIVES TOILET PAPER THIEF 40 YEARS IN CAN
Politicians rollin' in dough

Symphonies hit sour note
END THE VICIOUS DEBT CYCLE
An antidote to rising rents

GOODFELLAS HAVING GOOD TIME IN FEDERAL PEN

QUEEN OF THE DAMNED

I could never tell you—I'm too proud to admit
That you are the reason why I drink too much
I wish that I could just give it up and quit
But, when it wears off, I ache for your touch

You said that you loved me—you vowed you'd,
  never leave
I gave you everything! There's nothing left to take
Look! You made me a martyr and oh, how I grieve!
People think I'm strong; can't they see I'm a fake?

Love, you are the reason why I swallow too many
  pills
You crowned me the queen of the damned and
  tortured souls
So, I write about this world and all its social ills
And still, no one sees my bloody, gaping holes . . .

At night, the vampire
places a purple orchid
beside her tombstone

Pale skin, long black hair
Tight leather dress, combat boots
Smile reveals the fangs

THE PRISONER

I watched him
Shoot-up in the alley
Ah! How alike we are!
Both of us feeding
our addictions in filthy alleys
Creeping down city streets
At midnight, looking for
the fix to get us through
the long, lonely night.
I felt his alienation—
Indeed, he was in pain.
He did not suffer
when I fed on him.
No, he did not suffer . . .
He was freed from
his crippling addiction
His soul has transformed!
But . . .
I am still here
A prisoner of my own passion
Hiding in the dark corners,
Waiting
for my next prey.

The boy I wouldn't let break my heart...
Is a man now
Who holds my heart in the palm of his hand.
I want him to the point where I'm tortured!
Is he aware of the powerful hold he has on me?

Shamrocks in the spring
amongst the ancient tombstones
during the bombing

DEPRESSED IN VEGAS

It was supposed to be a fun, no holds barred weekend and for Harry, my best friend, I guess it was. We flew to Las Vegas so Harry could have one last fling before he tied the knot. He asked me to go with him and I jumped at the chance. I was working as a detective for the New York Police Department and well, New York in the winter time can really be one depressing son of a bitch! I wanted to go somewhere, anywhere where I could relax and yea, maybe have a fling myself. I never expected that I would return home even more depressed than when I left.

It all started when Harry came into the hotel room. That Saturday morning he got up before me and went out for a bit to see the sights while I slept. He returned with a brochure and threw it on the bed.

"Check it out, John. Pick any one, my treat. We're going there tonight. Come on, get up."

"I'm up. I just have to shower."

"Well...I'm gonna' check out the poker tables. Meet me downstairs in an hour, okay?"

"Sure."

Harry split and I decided to look through the brochure. It was an advertisement for a brothel and it had color photos of all the prostitutes available. At first I was aroused. The women were beautiful, almost too beautiful. One photo had a naked blonde woman with soap all over her body. Another had a topless, buxom chick licking her glossy, pink lips. I looked at these girls and wondered about them. Inside they must hate men, they would have to. How could they stand our dirty kinks and perverted quirks? A part of me felt sorry for these girls in the photos but I couldn't help being attracted to them. I wanted to sleep with all of them until I turned to page fifteen. That's when I saw her."

"No, it can't be," I thought. It was the spitting image of a girl I went to high school with named Charlotte Bernard.

"It's her," I realized. Those green eyes and that red hair I will never forget.

"Damn it! What happened to her? Why would she do this to herself?"

I remembered the way she was in history class. Kept to herself but was no snob—just different. I had a crush on her but I was going steady with a girl named Nancy. One day Charlotte asked me if I would like to go to the prom with her but I already promised Nancy we'd go together and...I'm a man of my word. I really wanted to go with Charlotte, though. She was cool. Really ahead of her time back then. She wore all black and was into Punk-Rock. Said she wanted to be a writer.

I looked at the photo of the girl I had a crush on in high school. She had on only a black lace garter belt with lace stockings and was licking the bedpost. That's when I became seriously depressed. I was depressed about poor Charlotte Bernard, disgusted with myself, and with the whole miserable, fucked-up world.

Lenape display
ancient wisdom encased
in glass, forgotten.

Bombs explode! While birds
and coyotes flee from death,
cacti weep in pain.

Oak tree in the park,
waves its doomed leaves to the sky . . .
saws break the silence.

THE MURDER OF EDEN

They took your life to print their lies
Forest green leaves no longer dance in the sky
You listened as others pleaded for their lives
While they mutilated you with powerful knives
They believed that you were unable to feel pain
And with your corpse they had so much to gain
They won't stop until each tree is dead
There's a profit for all of your heads
Precious Eden is now an old, forgotten song
Will they ever repay your soul for what they did
wrong?

EARTH MOURNING SONG

You took away our sacred land
And bled our great Mother dry
Still, it is for you, we cry

You, who forced us to take a stand
Our people were so proud to die—
How the four waken corners cried!

You, who poisoned our pure land
And made red explosions in the sky
Yes, it is for you, we cry

DIAMOND IN THE SKY

"Where are you going at this hour?" Carol asked as she watched her husband tie his sneakers.

"I feel restless. I'm going for a walk."

"At eleven o'clock at night? Gary, you're not going out to have a drink, are you? You can be honest with me, sweetheart. There's nothing we can't work out."

"You have no faith in me, Carol. No, I'm not going out for a drink. I need to clear my head. Remember what the doctor told us?"

"I do have faith in you. I can't help worrying about you, that's all."

"I promise I won't be gone too long." Gary kissed his wife on the head and left their bedroom. He grabbed his Yankees jacket from the hall closet and headed for the town cemetery.

Gary climbed through an old hole in the fence and looked around to make sure that no one was watching him. He took out the flashlight from his jacket and searched for a grave.

"There you are, Jimmy. I almost forgot about today. You'll be dead twenty years. I always remember your birthday. That's easy 'cause we're both born in the same month but...I guess it's hard for me to acknowledge the day you left us."

"Twenty years, Jimmy! I'm thirty seven now and yet, you're seventeen forever. I feel like an old man. My daughter started high school this year. What else can I tell you about? You probably can see everything that goes on, right? My job's a bitch. It's a livin' man. It pays the bills. I never did make it to the Major League. Remember when we were gonna' change the world of baseball? We were gonna' play for the Yankees."

"I miss those days. I don't have the dream anymore but at least I have my family. I wish you were here. There were so many things I wanted you to be a part of, you know? Like being the best man at my wedding. I wanted you to be Sara's godfather, too. You always looked out for me. Like that time Buddy Hansen called me 'midget man' 'cause I was so short and you beat the crap out of him for saying it. I wish I could have been there for you. You never gave me the chance."

"I can't believe you'd hang yourself over a goddamn game!" Gary cried. He wiped his face in anger.

"You were the one who was gonna' go places in life! You had the college scholarships, the chicks. Me, I was the ordinary one. I never went to college but you could have. But, in your senior year, you check out over a fuckin' baseball game. Coach Thompson was an asshole! He blamed the loss on you but it wasn't your fault."

"I still see your dad from time to time. I saw him at the ACME last month. I didn't know what to say to him, Jimmy. You were the one who was good with words. He still wears your baseball cap. He hugged me and cried. I smelt liquor on his breath. He's a broken man because his son couldn't accept any type of failure." Gary wiped his eyes with his sleeve and touched the gravestone.

"I hope there's a diamond in the sky for you. I can't picture you not playing ball. Maybe you even got to play with Babe Ruth."

"What else can I tell you? I'm sober. It's been eight months since I touched a drop of booze. I quit smoking, too. It's not easy but it's not as bad as I thought. I coach little league these days. I try to stress that it's not the end of the world if we lose a game. I don't want that kind of pressure on those little kids. Their parents get *obsessed* sometimes, so, I set them straight."

"You know, watching those kids play on the same field that we used to brings so much back to me. Sometimes, right before the sun sets, I'll be collecting the balls and see those two young boys who wanted to play for the Yankees."

"Well, I better get home. I wanted you to know that you're on my mind a lot. It's still hard without you."

Gary made the sign of the cross and remained silent for a minute.

"God, I could use a drink," he whispered.

When I recall you
holding me in your cellar
...I ache for you still

Our autumn shore trip
Swimming in a sea of ghosts
all of us. . . forlorned.

———∞∞∞———

The phantoms of fall
float above graveyard entrance
lonely for company.

The meadowlands are gone.
All corporate concrete white—
Suits where animals should be.

Ancient tombs hidden
beneath sand and cactus blooms;
diggers break the earth.

GHOST TRACKS

I think I saw a ghost earlier this evening.
I was walking on Orient Way with Black Elk's
words on my mind.

The sky was a dusky haze; it looked disturbed by
all that was occurring beneath its beauty,
and Hillside Cemetery
looked like it was on fire.
The tombstones glowed from all the attention
the fading sun bestowed upon their forgotten,
neglected images. The ghost (?) knelt beside
the entrance of the dead
and shot-up right in front of me—
Oblivious to everything around him.
The pain in his eyes haunted me; I knew it well.

Was his soul condemned to roam the earth as a
junkie-ghost? Did he choose this route?
We all have choices. (Yea, right.)
What did he want to be before he became a junkie?
Did those lost dead dreams creep inside his brain?
Is that what destroyed him?

I wanted to reach out to him—wanted
to take him in my arms and kiss away
his infected tracks
But . . .
I blinked away the black tear of liner
that bled from my eye
And—He was gone.
Perhaps, it was only the road-dust,
Manipulated by the wind.

Man on his car phone
hurls garbage out the window—
squirrel looks puzzled.

ASYLUM

"Mom, please listen to me. Visiting time is almost over. Dr. Kimbel is a sadist! He's the one who gave me the cigarette burns. Look for yourself!" Kelly turned around and lifted up her white tee shirt to reveal burn marks scattered across her back.

"How would I be able to burn myself in the back? He's the one who cut my hair off, too. I bit him while he forced me to give him a blow-job and he beat me and cut my hair off. Look at the bruises!" Kelly rolled up the short sleeves of her shirt and pointed to the dark black and blue circles on her upper arms.

"Kelly, Dr. Kimbel told me you would say those things. He said that all the male figures in your life had failed you, especially your father. He explained to me that you perceive him as a father figure so you say these terrible things to rebel against him. He also told me that you cut your hair off in a tantrum because the nurse wouldn't allow you to dye your hair."

"Mom, how would I get a hold of a pair of scissors to do that? We can't even have nail files on my floor. You know I would never cut my hair off just to prove a point. Listen to me, you have to get me out of here. I'm not crazy." Kelly knelt on the floor next to her mother's chair and grabbed her hand.

"Get you out of here? I took a second mortgage on the house just to get you in here. This place is your last chance. You're a delusional schizophrenic. You probably imagined Dr. Kimbel doing that to you and hurt yourself without remembering any of it."

"Why did I think I could get through to you? You didn't believe me when I told you about what Daddy used to do to make me do! The mother figures in my life failed me, too. You and all my female teachers. Sisterhood is a lie! Women don't look out for each other; they rip each other apart. You make me sick! You have me right where you want me—in hell. I'm in hell and my mother's paying to keep me here!" Kelly stood up and paced the room.

"How dare you? I've done all I can for you and now I'm getting on with my life! I've given you this opportunity to help yourself. You're not even the slightest bit grateful either, after all I've done for you."

"If you get me out of here, I promise I will never ask you for another thing."

"I promised Dr. Kimbel that I would not let you manipulate me. He said that you want to leave because you have an authority problem and you don't want to obey their rules and schedules. It's crucial for you to have this structure in your life, Kelly."

"Your thirty minutes are over, Mrs. Doyle," the hospital guard informed Kelly's mother. He left the small visiting room and stood outside the door.

"I'll see you next month, Kelly. Dr. Kimbel thinks it would be in your best interest for me to keep my distance. Once a month for thirty minutes seems to be all you can handle. I pray for you every night. I want you to be well again."

"Mom, you won't see me next month. I'll be dead by then. Promise me that you'll press charges against Dr. Kimbel and this whole negligent institution! Dr. Kimbel killed Angie. She didn't set herself on fire, he did it to her! God knows what he'll do to me."

Mrs. Doyle began to cry. "Oh Kelly, you're so troubled. I'll pray for you each night, sweetheart." She touched her daughter's pale cheek and kissed her on the forehead.

"This is the *last* time you'll ever see me again, Mom," Kelly sobbed. She held her mother tightly and then kissed her hand.

"I'm not crazy, Mom."

"I'll see you next month, Kelly."

"No you won't."

Mrs. Doyle exited the visiting room and her eyes continued to tear. She walked down the hall to the nurse's station.

"Hi, Dr. Finch, is Dr. Kimbel here?" Mrs. Doyle took a tissue from the box on the counter and wiped her eyes.

"No, he's not. Can I help you? You sound troubled."

"Oh, it's about Kelly. I want to give him my consent for the operation. I didn't want this to happen but after talking to her and seeing what she's done to her body, I feel she is a danger to herself."

"Fine. He'll be back on Monday. I'll tell his secretary to contact you. You're doing the right thing, Mrs. Doyle. She'll receive the *best* care here and the operation along with medication will enable us to do that."

"Yes, it's best for everyone," Mrs. Doyle agreed. She thanked Dr. Finch and walked to the elevator.

"I hope I'm doing the right thing," she sighed as she pressed the down button.

I WANT TO LIVE IN THE SKY

I want to live in the sky
Away from corporations and stores
Among the spirits who fly
And the eagles that soar

I want to live in the sky
In a bed of electric blue
Free from complaints and cries
Basking in the brilliant hue

I want to live in the sky
With the clouds and the sun
Liberated from obligations and ties
And endless tasks that must be done

I want to live in the sky
With the moon and the stars
Where there are no crimes, no lies
No pollution and no noisy cars.

He ignites incense
ghosts appear in swirls of smoke
and dance in the sky

DEEP IN SUBURBIA, '87

Deep in Suburbia...
   A woman parks her Mercedes down the street,
   By the church.
   Glares at a teenager.
   Using her upper-class manner
   Gold cross shining around her neck
   Shakes hands with the preacher
   The preacher who's looking down her shirt;
   The preacher who screams about nothing—
   Nothing at all...

Deep in Suburbia...
   A woman wearing her Calvin Klein nightgown
   Pushes her husband aside and turns off the light,
   Leaving him desperate because it's against her
   religion.
   She wonders why he leaves for the bar down the
   street.
   For each other, they feel nothing—
   Nothing at all...

Deep in Suburbia...
   A Vietnam Veteran is recognized by his
   "patriotic" town.
   The town that he and his best friend left to
   defend.
   The town that his best friend never returned to
   The town that shunned his return 20 years ago!
   The town he torments himself in.
   The town that has nothing—
   Nothing at all...

                    May 31, 1987

ANOTHER DAY AT THE OFFICE

"Ralph Turner speaking, how may I help you?"

"Are you a supervisor?"

"Yes ma'am."

"Well, it's about time! Now you listen here! I ordered a brass floor lamp from your company three months ago and it never came."

"Can I have your name and account number, please?"

"Miriam Stewart. My account number is 843291."

"Let me bring your account up on the screen." Turner typed the woman's last name and account number into the computer.

"Here we are. Miriam Stewart from the Bronx, correct?"

"Yes!" She screamed into the phone.

"The lamp was shipped out two weeks ago. You should have received it."

"Well, I haven't gotten anything!" Why two weeks ago when I ordered it three months ago?"

"The lamp was on back order because we were out of stock."

"Don't you notify your customers when that happens?"

"Yes. Usually we send out a postcard. I don't know why you never received that notice. I'll put a tracer on the package."

"How long will that take?"

"Oh, about two years," Turner replied.

"Very funny. I don't have time for your jokes, Mister. Can you put a new order in for me?"

"No."

"Why not?"

"Company policy. We can't put a new order in until we trace the first shipment."

"Your company stinks!"

"My sediments exactly."

"So, you're telling me I waited all this time for nothing?"

"Bingo."

"I don't like your attitude. You sound very unprofessional."

"Thank you, I try my best. Have a nice day." Turner disconnected the call. He stared at the gray walls of his sound-proof cubicle.

"What an eye soar," He grumbled. His cubicle was slightly larger than the other cubicles in the customer service department—one of the "perks" of his supervisory position.

"I feel like I'm in a cage," Turner sighed while he checked the messages on his voice mail.

"Hi, Ralph, Tony Rosa here. I received a call from a Mrs. Rogan, account number 952176 who said she's been trying to contact you for three weeks now. Pretty upset. Take care of it, okay? The number is 201-555-2125. Thanks."

"Good old pass the buck Tony. Sure I'll take care of her Mr. Do nothing vice president." Turner dialed the number.

"Good morning, is Mrs. Rogan there?"

"Speaking."

"Mrs. Rogan, this is Ralph Turner from the Home Delivery Club."

"Finally! I've been trying to get in touch with you for weeks. Your secretary takes my messages but you never call me back. That's why I called the vice president but he told me he couldn't help me but he'd make sure you took care of everything."

"Well, Mrs. Rogan, I'll be honest with you. I didn't want anyone to know but, my wife past away a few weeks ago and I haven't been in the right frame of mind these days. The work has really piled up on me. I'm trying my best."

"I'm so sorry to hear that. Oh, that's terrible. It makes my problems seem so minute."

"Yes, it certainly does. Hey, how about I call you in a couple of months to touch base, okay?"

"Wait, I need to---" Turner disconnected the call.

"Looks like I'm about due for a break," Turner glanced at his watch.

Turner made his way past the rows of gray cubicles and headed for the cafeteria. He laughed at the sign above the cafeteria entrance that stated: "HDC—Where Quality and Service are No. 1."

He was about to pour himself a cup of coffee when a member of his customer service team approached him. She was a short, heavy woman with neat, bobbed red hair.

"Hi, Ralph. Busy morning. So far, I've handled fifty calls. All delivery problems. What's going on with the shipments?"

"It's always the same old story, Sue. I worked my tail off this morning, too."

Turner finished his coffee and shook his head at the cafeteria's bright orange walls. The color was a subliminal attempt to stimulate the appetite of the workers but it just plain annoyed him. He crushed the paper coffee cup and hurled it into the trash. Break was over.

"Here's your mail, Ralph," Gina, his secretary placed the pile in the metal tray on his desk.

"Thanks," Turner smiled. He picked up the phone receiver and dialed his wife's telephone number.

"Hi, honey, it's me," Turner said as he took the contents of the metal tray and threw it in the garbage.

"Hi, Ralph. How's your day going?"

"Oh, just another day at the office, you know."

WAITRESS BLUES

I make the coffee and pour the hot tea
I change the Soup du Jour sign to split pea
 A man goes on about how lazy kids are today
  While I'm working two jobs for shit pay
I don't say a word
It's shit I've already heard
  Another man bitches that his food is cold
  So I tell the chef exactly what I'm told
The chef throws a fit
Now my head's gonna' split
  The woman at table three leaves me no tip
  It takes everything in me not to flip
My day is filled with complaints and moans
These assholes have fucking hearts of stone!
  I wish these people would just eat their meals
  And spare me the bitching and petty squeals
Yes, I know I'm paid to serve you
Secretly, I'm hoping you choke on what you chew
  I never hated anyone until I worked here
  Getting stuck here is my worst fear!
So, I'll listen to your lies
And pray the time flies
  I'm a waitress with the blues
  And a very short fuse
I feel like kicking the next customer's butt
So come in, order, eat, and keep your fucking mouth
  shut!

WHAT DID YOU DO TO DESERVE THIS?

I look at your picture.
Your eyes are
ulcerated and red.
Your body is confined
to a stock only to
reveal your head.
I think that perhaps
you must wonder
what you ever did that
was so unjust to
deserve this torture.

In the photo, I see a
light-haired man
wearing white. He is
holding an eyedropper
filled with fluid
standing over you (his
"instrument") waiting
to induce more
suffering in the name
of "beauty".

I can not help
wondering if you have
ever seen the light of
day. I think about
your existence and
question myself again
and again. Has this
creature always
existed in a lab? Was
it born in confinement
or was it taken from
Nature's way?

I am filled with agony
and sorrow for you. I
wish I could bring
your picture to life
and save you but I
know in reality, you
are helpless.

SHOCK TV

One of my friends called me three months ago to tell me to tape the S----Show because she and her husband were going to be guests on the show.

"It will be a clincher," she said.

"How so?" I asked.

"You'll see."

And did I ever! The topic of the show was infidelity and my friend lied to her husband and told him the topic of the show was spouse makeovers. So, this poor man is waiting backstage thinking that when he comes out he will see his wife with a new look.

Meantime, my friend is sitting center stage with another man who will remain present while she explains to her husband that she's had a three year affair with this man and wants a divorce so she can marry her lover.

The audience is all revved-up and the people are clapping and hollering—just waiting like voyeuristic vampires who feed off the shock and pain of others.

The talk show host coasts my friend with clichés like, "You're doing the right thing, it's time the truth came out," and I'm thinking, why can't she do this privately? Why does her husband have to be publicly humiliated like this? For the sake of a talk show's ratings? What have we become?

The audience can not be contained any longer so they bring my friend's husband out. He's smiling, probably wondering how his wife will look with a new style and then, they move in for the kill.

"Hey, you look the same," Jeff remarks to his wife. He sits in an empty seat next to her.

"*Jeff, Eva has something to tell you,*" *the talk show host informs him in this incredibly phony, soft voice.*

"*Jeff, I want a divorce. I've been having an affair with Will for the past three years and we want to be married.*" *The audience goes nuts. They scream, clap, whistle, hiss.*

Jeff sat there in disbelief. The crowd roared. People yelled: "Fool!" "Sucker!" "Busted!" "It's over!" Suddenly, Jeff rises from his chair and leaves the stage, much to the audience's delight. The host breaks for commercial.

For the record, I not close with her anymore. I am all for honesty but what she did to Jeff was degrading. It would be one thing if both parties understood what the topic was about and went on a talk show to discuss it, but it is beyond poor taste to deceive someone in order to get them on a talk show. Jeff had no idea what was waiting for him. Jeff is now suing her and the talk show and who knows how that will turn out.

I once thought that these so-called guests who bared all on many of these talk shows were paid actors but now I realize I was wrong. I used to think, why would anyone want to go on national television and air their dirty laundry like that? For money? Fame? I still don't get it. But most importantly, why do we care?

Woman in a fur
litters on Park Avenue
frowns at a beggar.

Mammoth sunflowers,
bathing in the warm sunbeams . . .
bulldozers nearby.

In the music store—
poster of The Lizard King
staring back at me.

Dreamt I heard your voice—
Woke from a deep sleep to find
A moth on my breast.

Fresh cut lavender
arranged in a purple vase,
beside the sickbed.

Elderly man walks
past children playing in the park
glances at his watch

I WANT TO WAKE THEM UP!

A world of trailer parks, minimum wage
    and shattered dreams
And broken hearts and everything's
    just as it seems
I know it well - been there too long
Since I fell - it's where I belong

I WANT TO WAKE THEM UP!

The broken, the battered, the tired, the weak
The anxious, the pretentious, the hopeless, the meek
But in their image I see my own
We mirror each other and I am thrown
I can not wake them because I'm asleep, too
Been this way for too long - don't know
    what to do . . .

I woke from a dip
into mysterious worlds
hidden within me